SNOOPY STARS

IN

THE MIXED DOUBLES

Charles M. Schulz

RAVETTE BOOKS

First published by
Ravette Books Limited 1989

Printed and bound in Great Britain
for Ravette Books Limited,
3 Glenside Estate, Star Road, Partridge Green,
Horsham, West Sussex RH13 8RA
by Cox & Wyman Ltd, Reading

ISBN 1 85304 172 6

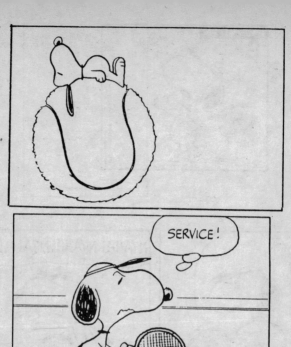

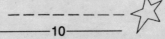

PEANUTS

HITTING BALLS AGAINST THE GARAGE AGAIN, I SEE...

I FIND IT INTERESTING THAT YOU SHOULD HAVE THE GARAGE FOR A PARTNER WHEN YOU PLAY MIXED-DOUBLES

9-16

I WAS ALSO WONDERING WHAT THE BEST PART OF HIS GAME IS...

HE NEVER FOOT-FAULTS!

SCHULZ

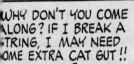

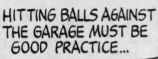

HITTING BALLS AGAINST THE GARAGE MUST BE GOOD PRACTICE...

5-3

IT'S PROBABLY ALSO FUN, ISN'T IT?

UNTIL SOMEONE PARKS THE CAR!

A TENNIS PRO ONCE SAID THAT YOU COULDN'T BE A CHAMPION UNTIL YOU HAD HIT TEN THOUSAND BALLS AGAINST THE GARAGE

THAT WASN'T A TENNIS PRO...

THAT WAS A GARAGE SALESMAN!

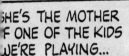

OKAY, WE'LL RECEIVE ON THIS SIDE

THAT'S NOT FAIR!

THAT MEANS WE HAVE THE SUN IN OUR EYES! WHY DO WE ALWAYS SERVE WITH THE SUN IN OUR EYES?!

7-5

SEE? DIDN'T I TELL YOU? "CRYBABY" BOOBIE COMPLAINS ABOUT EVERYTHING!

I THINK THE NET IS TOO HIGH! THESE BALLS FEEL DEAD! I CAN'T PLAY ON A SLOW COURT! THESE BALLS ARE TOO LIVELY! I THINK THE NET IS TOO LOW!

10-13

RATS!

HE WHO LIVES BY THE DIRTY ROTTEN LITTLE DROP SHOT, DIES BY THE DIRTY ROTTEN LITTLE DROP SHOT!

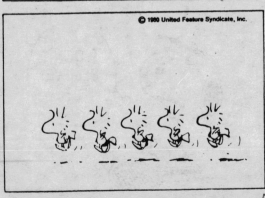

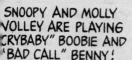

4-21

© 1982 United Feature Syndicate, Inc.

© 1988 United Feature Syndicate, Inc.

6-26

Other Snoopy titles published by Ravette Books

Snoopy Stars in this series

Colour landscapes

Weekenders

Black and white landscapes

It's a Dog's Life	£2.50
Roundup	£2.50
Freewheelin'	£2.50
Joe Cool	£2.50
Chariots For Hire	£2.50
Dogs Don't Eat Dessert	£2.50
You're on the Wrong Foot Again, Charlie Brown	£2.50
By Supper Possessed	£2.95
Talk is Cheep, Charlie Brown	£2.95

All these books are available at your local bookshop or news-agent, or can be ordered direct from the publisher. Just tick the titles you require and fill in the form below. Prices and availability subject to change without notice.

Ravette Books Limited, 3 Glenside Estate, Star Road, Partridge Green, Horsham, West Sussex RH13 8RA

Please send a cheque or postal order, and allow the following for postage and packing. UK: Pocket-books – 45p for one book, 20p for a second book and 15p for each additional book. Other titles – 50p for one book and 30p for each additional book.

Name ....

Address ....

....